The
Royal Horticultural Society
Diary 1999

JOHN LINDLEY (1799 - 1865)

Commentary by Brent Elliott

FRANCES LINCOLN

Frances Lincoln Limited
4 Torriano Mews
Torriano Avenue
London NW5 2RZ

The Royal Horticultural Society Diary 1999
Copyright © Frances Lincoln Limited 1998
All illustrations copyright © The Royal Horticultural Society 1998 and reproduced by courtesy of the RHS
Profits from the sale of this diary are an important contribution to the funds raised by the Royal Horticultural
Society, a registered charity.

Astronomical information reproduced, with permission, from data supplied by HM Nautical Almanac Office, copyright © Particle
Physics and Astronomy Research Council

British Library cataloguing-in-publication data
A catalogue record for this book is available from the British Library
ISBN 0-7112-1232-5
Typeset in Fairfield Light by Frances Lincoln Limited
Printed in Hong Kong
First Frances Lincoln edition: 1998

RHS FLOWER SHOWS 1999

All shows feature a wide range of floral exhibits staged by the nursery trade, with
associated competitions reflecting seasonal changes, and horticultural sundries.
With the exception of the shows at Malvern, Chelsea, Strathclyde, Birmingham,
Hampton Court, Tatton Park and Wisley, all RHS Flower Shows will be held in
one or both of the Society's Horticultural Halls in Greycoat Street and Vincent
Square, Westminster, London SW1.

*The dates given are correct at the time of going to press, but before travelling to a
Show we strongly advise you to check with the Diary Dates section of the RHS
Journal* The Garden, *or telephone the 24-hour Flower Show Information Line for
the latest details. Tel: 0171 649 1885.*

EUROPEAN NATIONAL HOLIDAYS 1999
Holidays that fall on a Sunday are not included

AUSTRIA	Jan. 1, 6; April 5; May 1, 13, 24; June 3; Oct. 26; Nov. 1; Dec. 8, 25
BELGIUM	Jan. 1; April 5; May 1, 13, 24; July 21; Nov. 1, 11; Dec. 25
DENMARK	Jan. 1; April 1, 2, 5, 30; May 13, 24; June 5; Dec. 24, 25
FINLAND	Jan. 1, 6; April 2, 5; May 1, 13; June 26; Nov. 6; Dec. 6, 25
FRANCE	Jan. 1; April 5; May 1, 8, 13, 24; July 14; Nov. 1, 11; Dec. 25
GERMANY	Jan. 1; April 2, 5; May 13; Nov. 17; Dec. 25
GREECE	Jan. 1, 6; Feb. 22; March 25; April 9, 12; May 1, 31; Oct. 28; Dec. 25
ITALY	Jan. 1, 6; April 5; May 1; Nov. 1; Dec. 8, 25
LUXEMBOURG	Jan. 1; April 5; May 1, 13, 24; June 23; Nov. 1; Dec. 25
NETHERLANDS	Jan. 1; April 2, 5, 30; May 13, 24; Dec. 25
NORWAY	Jan. 1; April 1, 2, 5; May 1, 13, 17, 24; Dec. 25
PORTUGAL	Jan. 1; Feb. 16; April 2; May 1; June 3, 10; Oct. 5; Nov. 1; Dec. 1, 8, 25
SPAIN	Jan. 1, 6; April 1, 2; May 1, 13; June 3; Oct. 12; Nov. 1; Dec. 6, 8, 25
SWEDEN	Jan. 1, 6; April 2, 5; May 1, 13, 24; June 26; Nov. 6; Dec. 25
SWITZERLAND	Jan. 1; April 2, 5; May 1, 13, 24; Dec. 25

JOHN LINDLEY

1799–1865

1999 sees the two hundredth anniversary of the birth of John Lindley, one of England's greatest botanists and probably the most eminent person ever to have been employed by the Royal Horticultural Society.

John Lindley was born on 5 February 1799. His father was George Lindley, a nurseryman at Catton, near Norwich, whose book *The Orchard and Kitchen Garden* John later edited for publication. In 1818 he went to London and, through his friend William Hooker, found employment helping with the arrangement of Robert Brown's herbarium in Sir Joseph Banks's library. After Banks's death in 1820, Lindley was hired by William Cattley of Barnet to publish the *Collectanea botanica*, a series of illustrations of plants from Cattley's collection.

In 1821, Lindley began working for the Horticultural Society as an artist, his specific brief being to draw roses. He excelled, and in the following year was appointed Assistant Secretary at the Society's new garden at Chiswick, his duties being 'to have superintendence over the collection of plants, and all other matters in the Garden'. It was at Chiswick that Lindley established shows with competitive classes, to which the origins of the modern flower show can be traced. It was also during this period that he wrote his first paper to be published in the Society's *Transactions*: 'A sketch of the principal tropical fruits which are likely to be worth cultivating in England for the dessert' (volume V, 1821–1822). In 1827 he was elevated to the position of Assistant Secretary to the Society as a whole, with duties at both Chiswick and its London offices. As Assistant Secretary he also acted as the editor of the Society's publications – first the *Transactions*, and then the *Journal*. In 1841 he was appointed Vice-Secretary to the Society.

One of his specialities was the identification of plants sent back by the Society's collectors. From the 1820s to the 1840s, the Society sent emissaries to every continent to discover new plants of potential garden interest. Among them were John Damper Parks, who introduced yellow roses from China; Theodor Hartweg, who brought back the ancestors of the modern fuchsia from Mexico; Robert Fortune, who made his first expedition to China for the Society; and best known of all, David Douglas, after whom the Douglas fir was named. Lindley's work on the plants these explorers sent back resulted in a wide range of new plant names being coined. Some of the plants are illustrated in the following pages.

His work for the Society did not prevent Lindley from accepting a range of duties elsewhere. At the age of twenty-nine he was elected Professor of Botany at the newly founded University of London, a post he held for over thirty years. From 1835 to 1853 he was also Professor of Botany to the Society of

Apothecaries, a role which brought with it the responsibility of being director of the Chelsea Physic Garden.

Lindley's name as an horticultural editor grew through work outside the Society. From late in 1827 until 1830, he edited the *Pomological Magazine*, a fruit journal modelled in format on Curtis's *Botanical Magazine*. In 1815, Sydenham Edwards, a former artist for Curtis, had started a rival magazine called the *Botanical Register*, and Lindley became its editor in 1829. One of the earliest published accounts of Australian plants, Lindley's important 'Sketch of the vegetation of the Swan River [an Australian colony]' appeared in this magazine in 1839. Then, together with Joseph Paxton, he founded the *Gardeners' Chronicle* in 1841 and *Paxton's Flower Garden* (three volumes, 1850–1853). The former became the longest-running horticultural periodical, and Lindley remained editor until his death.

Lindley's spectacular energy and enthusiasm involved him in further extra-curricular activities. In 1838 he compiled a report on the condition of the royal gardens at Kew, which led to the establishment of the Royal Botanic Gardens, of which his old friend William Hooker was made the first Director. He was also active on the 1845 commission to enquire into the causes of the Irish potato blight; a juror for food products at the Great Exhibition of 1851; and for many years he was consulted by the Admiralty about the planting of the island of Ascension.

Lindley's great passion for the family of the Orchidaceae began with his work for William Cattley, after whom he named the genus *Cattleya*. He was the first botanist to work out a classification of orchids, and wrote prolifically on the subject, his most notable works being the *Sertum orchidaceum* (1838–1841) and *The Genera and Species of Orchidaceous Plants* (1830–1840). He coined the names of approximately eighty orchid genera still recognised today, including *Cattleya*, *Coelogyne*, *Laelia*, *Lycaste* and *Miltonia*. He has been called the father of modern orchidology, and the American Orchid Society named its scientific journal *Lindleyana* in his honour.

Among his numerous other works were: *Rosarum monographia* (1820); *Digitalium monographia* (1821); *Synopsis of the British Flora* (1829); *Introduction to the Natural System of Botany* (1830); *Fossil Flora of Great Britain* with William Hutton (1831–1837), long the standard work in English; *Ladies' Botany* (1834); *Key to Structural and Systematic Botany* (1835); the text for the last volumes of Sibthorp's *Flora Graeca* (1835–1837); *Victoria Regia* (1837); *Flora Medica* (1838); *Theory of Horticulture* (1840); *Elements of Botany* (1841); *The Vegetable Kingdom* (1846); and the initial botanical text for E. J. Ravenscroft's *Pinetum Britannicum* (1863).

In 1858 Lindley was finally promoted to Secretary of the Society. He held the office during the period when its name was changed to the Royal Horticultural

Society. Failing health brought his contribution to public life to an end after he helped organize the Great Exhibition of 1862. This sequel to the exhibition of 1851 was held in the RHS's new gardens in Kensington. On his retirement a public subscription was raised for him, and E.V. Eddis painted his portrait, which now hangs in the library named after him. After an incredibly full life, his last years were spent suffering from a failing memory and 'softening of the brain'; he died on 31 October 1865.

Lindley left an unintended double legacy to the world. He married in 1823 and had three children, and for several years the Lindley family lived at Bedford House, Acton, near the Society's garden. After his death, this estate became the site of London's first garden suburb, Bedford Park, the course of whose streets was planned in order to preserve as many of Lindley's trees as possible.

His second legacy was the Lindley Library. In 1859 the Horticultural Society sold its library during a period of financial retrenchment. When it could afford to begin to replace this loss, using profits from the International Botanical Congress and Horticultural Exhibition, the Society purchased Lindley's personal library to serve as the nucleus of a new collection. In 1868, the library was invested in the Lindley Library Trust (which is now administered by the RHS as sole Trustee) in order to ensure that it could never be sold again. Lindley's acquisitions now form the cornerstone of the world's greatest horticultural library.

Of the plants named after Lindley the following are still available : *Aeonium lindleyi, Buddleja lindleyana, Corydalis lindleyana, Photinia lindleyana, Rhododendron lindleyi* and *Salix lindleyana*. There are other plants currently available that were once named after Lindley, but which are now known by other names: *Bignonia lindleyana* (now *Clytostoma callistegioides*) and *Sorbaria lindleyana* (now *S. tomentosa*).

Brent Elliott
The Royal Horticultural Society

Front cover

Tacsonia (now *Passiflora*) *manicata*, a hand-retouched chromolithograph by Louis-Aristide-Léon Constans (*fl.* 1830s–1860s), from the first volume of *Paxton's Flower Garden* (1850–1851) by John Lindley and Joseph Paxton

Title page

The 'Cannon Hall Muscat' grape, a hand-coloured engraving after a drawing by Augusta Innes Withers (1792–1869), from the *Transactions of the Horticultural Society* (1832), in which the fruit was described for the first time by John Lindley.

December 1998 & January 1999

28 MONDAY

Holiday, UK, Republic of Ireland,
Canada, Australia and New Zealand

29 TUESDAY

30 WEDNESDAY

31 THURSDAY

1 FRIDAY

New Year's Day
Holiday, UK, Republic of Ireland,
Canada, USA, Australia and New Zealand

2 SATURDAY   *Full Moon*

3 SUNDAY

Cattleya loddigesii, a hand-coloured engraving after a drawing by John Lindley, from his *Collectanea botanica* (1821). Both the genus and the species were named by Lindley.

4   MONDAY   *Holiday, Scotland and New Zealand*

5   TUESDAY

6   WEDNESDAY   *Epiphany*

7   THURSDAY

8   FRIDAY

9   SATURDAY   *Last Quarter*

10   SUNDAY

Crocus pusillus (now *C. biflorus*), a hand-coloured engraving after a drawing by Miss S. A. Drake (*fl.* 1820s–1840s), from the 23rd volume of the *Botanical Register* (1837), edited by John Lindley

January WEEK 2

11   MONDAY

12   TUESDAY

13   WEDNESDAY

14   THURSDAY

15   FRIDAY

16   SATURDAY

17   SUNDAY   *New Moon*

Berberis nepalensis (now *vulgaris*), a hand-retouched chromolithograph by Louis-Aristide-Léon Constans (*fl.* 1830s–1860s), from the third volume of *Paxton's Flower Garden* (1852–1853) by John Lindley and Joseph Paxton

18 MONDAY   *Holiday, USA (Martin Luther King's birthday)*

19 TUESDAY   *RHS Flower Show*

20 WEDNESDAY   *RHS Flower Show*

21 THURSDAY

22 FRIDAY

23 SATURDAY

24 SUNDAY   *First Quarter*

Helleborus atrorubens, a hand-retouched chromolithograph by Louis-Aristide-Léon Constans
(*fl.* 1830s–1860s), from the third volume of *Paxton's Flower Garden* (1852–1853) by John Lindley
and Joseph Paxton

January WEEK 4

25 MONDAY

26 TUESDAY   *Holiday, Australia (Australia Day)*

27 WEDNESDAY

28 THURSDAY

29 FRIDAY

30 SATURDAY

31 SUNDAY   *Full Moon*

Garrya elliptica, a hand-coloured engraving after a drawing by Miss S. A. Drake (*fl.* 1820s–1840s), from the 20th volume of the *Botanical Register* (1834–1835), edited by John Lindley. This plant was discovered by the Horticultural Society's collector David Douglas and first described by Lindley.

1 MONDAY

2 TUESDAY

3 WEDNESDAY

4 THURSDAY

5 FRIDAY

6 SATURDAY *Holiday, New Zealand (Waitangi Day)*

7 SUNDAY

Disa grandiflora, a hand-coloured engraving after a drawing by Miss S. A. Drake (*fl.* 1820s–1840s), from John Lindley's *Sertum orchidaceum* (1838–1841)

February Week 6

WEEK 6

8   MONDAY   *Last Quarter*

9   TUESDAY

10   WEDNESDAY

11   THURSDAY

12   FRIDAY   *Holiday, USA (Lincoln's birthday)*

13   SATURDAY

14   SUNDAY   *St Valentine's Day*

Now known as *Sequoiadendron giganteum*, this tree was named *Wellingtonia gigantea* by John Lindley in 1853. The chromolithograph was published in 1884 in the *Pinetum Britannicum*, edited by E. J. Ravenscroft; Lindley had been a collaborator when the work was begun in 1863.

15 MONDAY   *Holiday, USA (Presidents' Day)*

16 TUESDAY   *New Moon*   *Shrove Tuesday*
                                                                  Chinese New Year
                                                                  RHS Flower Show

17 WEDNESDAY   *Ash Wednesday*
                                                                  RHS Flower Show

18 THURSDAY

19 FRIDAY

20 SATURDAY

21 SUNDAY

Astrapaea wallichii, a hand-coloured engraving after a drawing by John Lindley from his
Collectanea botanica (1821)

February Week 8

22 MONDAY   *Washington's birthday, USA*

23 TUESDAY   *First Quarter*

24 WEDNESDAY

25 THURSDAY

26 FRIDAY

27 SATURDAY

28 SUNDAY

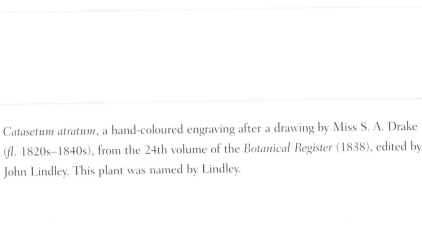

Catasetum atratum, a hand-coloured engraving after a drawing by Miss S. A. Drake (*fl.* 1820s–1840s), from the 24th volume of the *Botanical Register* (1838), edited by John Lindley. This plant was named by Lindley.

1 MONDAY   *St David's Day, Wales*

2 TUESDAY   *Full Moon*

3 WEDNESDAY

4 THURSDAY

5 FRIDAY

6 SATURDAY

7 SUNDAY

Forsythia viridissima, an unsigned chromolithograph from the second volume of *Jardin Fleuriste* (1851–1852) by Charles Lemaire, whose principal artist was Jean-Christophe Heyland (1792–1866). This plant was named and described by John Lindley in 1847.

March WEEK 10

8   MONDAY   *Commonwealth Day*

....

9   TUESDAY

....

10 WEDNESDAY   *Last Quarter*

....

11 THURSDAY

....

12 FRIDAY

....

13 SATURDAY

....

14 SUNDAY   *Mothering Sunday*

....

Cypripedium (now *Paphiopedilum*) *purpuratum*, a hand-coloured engraving after a drawing by Miss S. A. Drake (*fl.* 1820s–1840s), from the 23rd volume of the *Botanical Register* (1837), edited by John Lindley

15 MONDAY

16 TUESDAY   *RHS Flower Show*

17 WEDNESDAY   *New Moon*   *St Patrick's Day, Ireland*
                                                            Holiday, Northern Ireland and Republic of Ireland
                                                                                                RHS Flower Show

18 THURSDAY

19 FRIDAY

20 SATURDAY   *RHS Orchid Show*

21 SUNDAY   *Vernal Equinox*
                                                                                                        RHS Orchid Show

Erythronium grandiflorum, a hand-coloured engraving after a drawing by Miss S. A. Drake (*fl.* 1820s–1840s), from the 21st volume of the *Botanical Register* (1836), edited by John Lindley. This plant was discovered by the Horticultural Society's collector David Douglas and named by Lindley.

March   WEEK 12

22 MONDAY

23 TUESDAY

24 WEDNESDAY   *First Quarter*

25 THURSDAY

26 FRIDAY

27 SATURDAY

28 SUNDAY

Palm Sunday
British Summer Time begins
(subject to confirmation)

Brownea ariza, the Ariza plant, a hand-retouched chromolithograph by Louis-Aristide-Léon Constans (*fl.* 1830s–1860s), from the second volume of *Paxton's Flower Garden* (1851–1852) by John Lindley and Joseph Paxton. The plant was collected by Theodor Hartweg for the Horticultural Society.

March & April

29 MONDAY

30 TUESDAY

31 WEDNESDAY   *Full Moon*

1 THURSDAY   *Maundy Thursday*
                                                              Passover (Pesach) First Day

2 FRIDAY   *Good Friday*

3 SATURDAY

4 SUNDAY   *Easter Sunday*

Amaryllis solandraeflora (now *Hippeastrum solandraeflorum*), a hand-coloured engraving from John Lindley's
Collectanea botanica (1821), of a plant both named and drawn by Lindley (from William Cattley's
specimen)

5 MONDAY

Easter Monday
Holiday, UK (exc. Scotland), Republic of Ireland,
Canada, Australia and New Zealand

6 TUESDAY

7 WEDNESDAY

Passover (Pesach) Seventh Day

8 THURSDAY

Passover (Pesach) Eighth Day

9 FRIDAY   *Last Quarter*

10 SATURDAY

11 SUNDAY

Camellia reticulata, a hand-coloured engraving after a drawing by Alfred Chandler (1804–1896), from *Illustrations and Descriptions of the Plants which Compose the Natural Order Camellieae* (1831) by Chandler and William Beattie Booth. This plant was introduced into England by the Horticultural Society's collector John Damper Parks in 1824 and was named by John Lindley.

12 MONDAY

13 TUESDAY   *RHS Flower Show*

14 WEDNESDAY   *RHS Flower Show*

15 THURSDAY

16 FRIDAY   *New Moon*

17 SATURDAY   *Islamic New Year (subject to sighting of moon)*

18 SUNDAY

Primula sinensis, a hand-coloured engraving from John Lindley's *Collectanea botanica* (1821) of a plant both named and drawn by Lindley

April

19 MONDAY

20 TUESDAY

21 WEDNESDAY   *Birthday of Queen Elizabeth II*

22 THURSDAY   *First Quarter*

23 FRIDAY   *St George's Day, England*

24 SATURDAY

25 SUNDAY   *Holiday, Australia and New Zealand (Anzac Day)*

Varieties of *Tulipa scabriscapa*, a hand-coloured engraving after a drawing by Miss S. A. Drake
(*fl.* 1820s–1840s), from the 23rd volume of the *Botanical Register* (1837), edited by John Lindley

April & May

---

26 MONDAY

---

27 TUESDAY   *RHS Flower Show*

---

28 WEDNESDAY   *RHS Flower Show*

---

29 THURSDAY

---

30 FRIDAY   *Full Moon*

---

1 SATURDAY

---

2 SUNDAY

Myosotis azorica, the Azorean Forget-me-not, a hand-retouched chromolithograph by Louis-Aristide-Léon Constans (*fl.* 1830s–1860s), from the third volume of *Paxton's Flower Garden* (1852–1853) by John Lindley and Joseph Paxton

May

3   MONDAY   *May Day Holiday, UK (exc. Scotland) and Republic of Ireland*
Spring Holiday, Scotland

4   TUESDAY

5   WEDNESDAY

6   THURSDAY   *Malvern Spring Gardening Show preview*
(to be confirmed)

7   FRIDAY   *Malvern Spring Gardening Show*

8   SATURDAY   *Last Quarter*   *Malvern Spring Gardening Show*

9   SUNDAY   *Mother's Day, Canada and USA*
Malvern Spring Gardening Show

Rosa macrophylla, a hand-coloured engraving after a drawing by John Lindley from his *Rosarum monographia* (1820)

10 MONDAY

11 TUESDAY

12 WEDNESDAY

13 THURSDAY — *Ascension Day*

14 FRIDAY

15 SATURDAY — *New Moon*

16 SUNDAY

Now known as *Kennedia prostrata*, this plant was named *K. maryattae* by John Lindley. The hand-coloured engraving, after a drawing by Miss S. A. Drake (*fl.* 1820s–1840s), was published in the 21st volume of the *Botanical Register* (1836), edited by Lindley.

May   WEEK 20

17 MONDAY

18 TUESDAY

19 WEDNESDAY

20 THURSDAY

21 FRIDAY   *Jewish Feast of Weeks (Shavuot)*

22 SATURDAY   *First Quarter*

23 SUNDAY   *Whit Sunday (Pentecost)*

The 'Turkey' apricot, a hand-coloured engraving after a drawing by Augusta Innes Withers (1792–1869), from the first volume of John Lindley's *Pomological Magazine* (1827–1828)

24 MONDAY

Holiday, Canada (Victoria Day)

25 TUESDAY

Chelsea Flower Show

26 WEDNESDAY

Chelsea Flower Show

27 THURSDAY

Chelsea Flower Show

28 FRIDAY

Chelsea Flower Show

29 SATURDAY

30 SUNDAY   *Full Moon*

Trinity Sunday

The graft-hybrid + *Laburnocytisus* 'Adami', a hand-coloured engraving after a drawing by Miss S. A. Drake (*fl.* 1820s–1840s), from the 23rd volume of the *Botanical Register* (1837), edited by John Lindley

31 MONDAY

Spring Holiday, UK (exc. Scotland)
May Day Holiday, Scotland
Holiday, USA (Memorial Day)

1 TUESDAY

2 WEDNESDAY

3 THURSDAY

Corpus Christi

4 FRIDAY

National Gardening Show, Strathclyde

5 SATURDAY

National Gardening Show, Strathclyde

6 SUNDAY

National Gardening Show, Strathclyde

Odontoglossum laeve, a chromolithograph after a drawing by Walter Hood Fitch (1817–1892) of an orchid named by John Lindley and published in James Bateman's *Monograph of Odontoglossum* (1874)

7 MONDAY *Last Quarter*

8 TUESDAY

9 WEDNESDAY

10 THURSDAY

11 FRIDAY

12 SATURDAY

The Queen's official birthday
(subject to confirmation)

13 SUNDAY *New Moon*

The 'deep blood-coloured moutan' (a variety of *Paeonia suffruticosa*), a hand-retouched chromolithograph by Louis-Aristide-Léon Constans (*fl.* 1830s–1860s), from the first volume of *Paxton's Flower Garden* (1850–1851) by John Lindley and Joseph Paxton

June WEEK 24

---

14 MONDAY

---

15 TUESDAY

---

16 WEDNESDAY   *BBC Gardeners' World Live, Birmingham, 16th-20th*

---

17 THURSDAY

---

18 FRIDAY

---

19 SATURDAY

---

20 SUNDAY   *First Quarter*   *Father's Day, UK, Canada and USA*

Gooseberry 'Crompton's Sheba Queen', a hand-coloured engraving after a drawing by Augusta Innes Withers (1792–1869), from the first volume of John Lindley's *Pomological Magazine* (1827–1828)

21 MONDAY — — — — — — — — — — — — — — — — *Summer Solstice*

22 TUESDAY — — — — — — — — — — — — — — — — *RHS Flower Show*

23 WEDNESDAY — — — — — — — — — — — — — — — — *RHS Flower Show*

24 THURSDAY

25 FRIDAY

26 SATURDAY

27 SUNDAY

Papaver bracteatum, a hand-coloured engraving from John Lindley's *Collectanea botanica* (1821), of a plant both named and drawn by Lindley

June & July

28 MONDAY *Full Moon*

29 TUESDAY

30 WEDNESDAY

1 THURSDAY *Holiday, Canada (Canada Day)*

2 FRIDAY

3 SATURDAY

4 SUNDAY *Independence Day, USA*

Allium caeruleum, a hand-coloured engraving after a drawing by Miss S. A. Drake (*fl.* 1820s–1840s), from the 26th volume of the *Botanical Register* (1840), edited by John Lindley

2

3

1

5 MONDAY

Holiday, USA (observed)
Hampton Court Palace Flower Show preview
(to be confirmed)

6 TUESDAY   *Last Quarter*

Hampton Court Palace Flower Show

7 WEDNESDAY

Hampton Court Palace Flower Show

8 THURSDAY

Hampton Court Palace Flower Show

9 FRIDAY

Hampton Court Palace Flower Show

10 SATURDAY

Hampton Court Palace Flower Show

11 SUNDAY

Hampton Court Palace Flower Show

Mandevilla suaveolens, a hand-coloured engraving after a drawing by Miss S. A. Drake (*fl.* 1820s–1840s), from the 26th volume of the *Botanical Register* (1840), edited by John Lindley. This plant was named by Lindley.

July WEEK 28

....

12 MONDAY   *Holiday, Northern Ireland (Battle of the Boyne)*

....

13 TUESDAY   *New Moon*

....

14 WEDNESDAY

....

15 THURSDAY   *St Swithin's Day*

....

16 FRIDAY

....

17 SATURDAY

....

18 SUNDAY

....

The 'Barnet' raspberry, a hand-coloured engraving after a drawing by Augusta Innes Withers (1792–1869), from the first volume of John Lindley's *Pomological Magazine* (1827–1828)

19 MONDAY

20 TUESDAY *First Quarter*

21 WEDNESDAY

22 THURSDAY *North West Show, Tatton Park*

23 FRIDAY *North West Show, Tatton Park*

24 SATURDAY *North West Show, Tatton Park*

25 SUNDAY *North West Show, Tatton Park*

Iris alata (now *planifolia*), a hand-coloured engraving after a drawing by Miss S. A. Drake (*fl.* 1820s–1840s), from the 22nd volume of the *Botanical Register* (1836), edited by John Lindley

26 MONDAY

27 TUESDAY

28 WEDNESDAY   *Full Moon*

29 THURSDAY

30 FRIDAY

31 SATURDAY

1 SUNDAY

Rosa woodsii, an original drawing in watercolour by John Lindley, dated 1821. Lindley named this species in 1820 from a specimen from the Missouri River area.

August

---

2   MONDAY

Summer Holiday, Scotland
Holiday, Republic of Ireland

---

3   TUESDAY

---

4   WEDNESDAY   *Last Quarter*

---

5   THURSDAY

---

6   FRIDAY

---

7   SATURDAY

---

8   SUNDAY

Clematis lanuginosa, a hand-retouched chromolithograph by Louis-Aristide-Léon Constans
(*fl.* 1830s–1860s), from the third volume of *Paxton's Flower Garden* (1852–1853) by John Lindley
and Joseph Paxton. This species had first flowered in cultivation that year, in the nursery of
Standish and Noble.

August WEEK 32

9   MONDAY

10   TUESDAY   *RHS Flower Show*

11   WEDNESDAY   *New Moon*   *RHS Flower Show*

12   THURSDAY

13   FRIDAY

14   SATURDAY

15   SUNDAY

Rosa sulphurea (now *R. hemisphaerica*), a hand-coloured engraving after a drawing by John Curtis (1791–1862), from John Lindley's *Rosarum monographia* (1820)

16 MONDAY

17 TUESDAY

18 WEDNESDAY

19 THURSDAY   *First Quarter*

20 FRIDAY

21 SATURDAY

22 SUNDAY

Tacsonia (now *Passiflora*) *manicata*, a hand-retouched chromolithograph by Louis-Aristide-Léon Constans (*fl.* 1830s–1860s), from the first volume of *Paxton's Flower Garden* (1850–1851) by John Lindley and Joseph Paxton

August WEEK 34

23 MONDAY

24 TUESDAY

25 WEDNESDAY

26 THURSDAY   *Full Moon*

27 FRIDAY

28 SATURDAY

29 SUNDAY

Digitalis ambigua (now *grandiflora*), a hand-coloured engraving after a drawing by Ferdinand Bauer (1760–1826), from John Lindley's *Digitalium monographia* (1821)

30 MONDAY   *Summer Holiday, UK (exc. Scotland)*

31 TUESDAY

1 WEDNESDAY

2 THURSDAY   *Last Quarter*

3 FRIDAY

4 SATURDAY

5 SUNDAY

Clematis florida 'Bicolor', a hand-coloured engraving after a drawing by Miss S. A. Drake (fl. 1820s–1840s), from the 24th volume of the *Botanical Register* (1838), edited by John Lindley

September WEEK 36

6 MONDAY *Holiday, Canada (Labour Day) and USA (Labor Day)*

7 TUESDAY

8 WEDNESDAY

9 THURSDAY *New Moon*

10 FRIDAY

11 SATURDAY *Jewish New Year (Rosh Hashanah)*

12 SUNDAY

Anemone japonica, a hand-coloured engraving after a drawing by Miss S. A. Drake
(*fl.* 1820s–1840s), from the 31st volume of the *Botanical Register* (1845), edited by John
Lindley. Although described in the 18th century, it was not grown in England until
Robert Fortune introduced it through the Horticultural Society in 1844.

September

---

13 MONDAY

---

14 TUESDAY   *RHS Great Autumn Show*

---

15 WEDNESDAY   *RHS Great Autumn Show*

---

16 THURSDAY

---

17 FRIDAY   *First Quarter*

---

18 SATURDAY

---

19 SUNDAY

Canna speciosa (now *C. coccinea*), a hand-coloured engraving by M. Hart, from the 15th volume of the *Botanical Register* (1829), the first volume to be edited by John Lindley

September

20 MONDAY   *Jewish Day of Atonement (Yom Kippur)*

21 TUESDAY

22 WEDNESDAY

23 THURSDAY   *Autumnal Equinox*

24 FRIDAY

25 SATURDAY   *Full Moon*   *Jewish Festival of Tabernacles (Succoth) First Day*
                                                                  Malvern Autumn Show

26 SUNDAY   *Malvern Autumn Show*

Passiflora × caeruleoracemosa (now *P. × violacea*), the first hybrid passion flower; a hand-coloured engraving after a drawing by John Lindley, from the *Transactions of the Horticultural Society* (1820)

September & October

27 MONDAY

28 TUESDAY

29 WEDNESDAY *Michaelmas Day*

30 THURSDAY

1 FRIDAY *Wisley Flower Show to take place in October*
(dates to be confirmed)

2 SATURDAY *Last Quarter* *Jewish Festival of Tabernacles (Succoth) Eighth Day*

3 SUNDAY

Sollya linearis, a hand-coloured engraving after a drawing by Miss S. A. Drake (*fl.* 1820s–1840s), from the 26th volume of the *Botanical Register* (1840), edited by John Lindley, who also named the plant

October WEEK 40

....

4   MONDAY

....

5   TUESDAY   *RHS Flower Show*

....

6   WEDNESDAY   *RHS Flower Show*

....

7   THURSDAY

....

8   FRIDAY

....

9   SATURDAY   *New Moon*

....

10 SUNDAY

....

Laelia superbiens, a species named by John Lindley but now included in the genus *Schomburgkia*. This hand-retouched chromolithograph after a drawing by Miss S. A. Drake (*fl.* 1820s–1840s), is from *The Orchidaceae of Mexico and Guatemala* (1843) by James Bateman (1811–1897).

11 MONDAY

12 TUESDAY

13 WEDNESDAY

14 THURSDAY

15 FRIDAY

16 SATURDAY

17 SUNDAY   *First Quarter*

Oxyramphis (now *Lespedeza*) *macrostyla*, a hand-coloured engraving after a drawing by Miss S. A. Drake (*fl.* 1820s–1840s), from the 32nd volume of the *Botanical Register* (1846), edited by John Lindley. This plant was introduced into England through the Horticultural Society in 1845.

October WEEK 42

18 MONDAY

19 TUESDAY

20 WEDNESDAY

21 THURSDAY

22 FRIDAY

23 SATURDAY

24 SUNDAY   *Full Moon*   *United Nations Day*

Hibiscus syriacus var. *chinensis*, a hand-retouched chromolithograph by Louis-Aristide-Léon Constans (*fl.* 1830s–1860s), from the third volume of *Paxton's Flower Garden* (1852–1853) by John Lindley and Joseph Paxton

25 MONDAY

26 TUESDAY

27 WEDNESDAY

28 THURSDAY

29 FRIDAY

30 SATURDAY

31 SUNDAY   *Last Quarter*

British Summer Time ends (subject to confirmation)
Hallowe'en

Mimulus cardinalis, a hand-coloured engraving, after a drawing by Miss S. A. Drake (*fl.* 1820s–1840s), from the *Transactions of the Horticultural Society* (1835). The plant was discovered and named by the Horticultural Society's collector David Douglas, and John Lindley published the first description.

November WEEK 44

1	MONDAY	*All Saints' Day*

2	TUESDAY	*RHS Flower Show*

3	WEDNESDAY	*RHS Flower Show*

4	THURSDAY	

5	FRIDAY	*Guy Fawkes' Day*

6	SATURDAY	

7	SUNDAY	

Mucuna pruriens, a hand-coloured engraving after a drawing by Miss S. A. Drake (*fl.* 1820s–1840s), from the 24th volume of the *Botanical Register* (1838), edited by John Lindley

8   MONDAY   *New Moon*

9   TUESDAY

10 WEDNESDAY

11 THURSDAY   *Holiday, Canada (Remembrance Day) and USA (Veterans' Day)*

12 FRIDAY

13 SATURDAY

14 SUNDAY   *Remembrance Sunday*

Portulaca thellusonii, a hand-coloured engraving after a drawing by Miss S. A. Drake (*fl.* 1820s–1840s), from the 26th volume of the *Botanical Register* (1840), edited by John Lindley. This plant was named by Lindley.

November

15 MONDAY

16 TUESDAY   *First Quarter*

17 WEDNESDAY

18 THURSDAY

19 FRIDAY

20 SATURDAY

21 SUNDAY

The 'Common Muscadine' grape, a hand-coloured engraving after a drawing by Augusta Innes Withers (1792–1869), from the first volume of John Lindley's *Pomological Magazine* (1827–1828)

November

---

22 MONDAY

---

23 TUESDAY *Full Moon* *RHS Flower Show*
(to be confirmed)

---

24 WEDNESDAY *RHS Flower Show*
(to be confirmed)

---

25 THURSDAY *Holiday, USA (Thanksgiving Day)*

---

26 FRIDAY

---

27 SATURDAY

---

28 SUNDAY *Advent Sunday*

Grammatophyllum speciosum, a hand-retouched chromolithograph by Louis-Aristide-Léon Constans (*fl.* 1830s–1860s), from the second volume of *Paxton's Flower Garden* (1851–1852) by John Lindley and Joseph Paxton

November & December

29 MONDAY   *Last Quarter*

30 TUESDAY   *St Andrew's Day, Scotland*

1   WEDNESDAY

2   THURSDAY

3   FRIDAY

4   SATURDAY   *Jewish Festival of Chanukah, First Day*

5   SUNDAY

Now known as *Encyclia vitellina*, this orchid was named *Epidendrum vitellinum* by John Lindley. The hand-coloured engraving after a drawing by Miss S. A. Drake (*fl.* 1820s–40s), is from Lindley's *Sertum orchidaceum* (1838–1841).

December

6   MONDAY

7   TUESDAY   *New Moon*

8   WEDNESDAY

9   THURSDAY   *Ramadân begins (subject to sighting of moon)*

10 FRIDAY

11 SATURDAY   *Jewish Festival of Chanukah, Eighth Day*

12 SUNDAY

Dendrobium caerulescens (now *D. nobile*), a hand-coloured engraving after a drawing by Miss S. A. Drake (*fl.* 1820s–1840s), from John Lindley's *Sertum orchidaceum* (1838–1841)

December week 50

13 MONDAY

14 TUESDAY   *RHS Christmas Show*

15 WEDNESDAY   *RHS Christmas Show*

16 THURSDAY   *First Quarter*

17 FRIDAY

18 SATURDAY

19 SUNDAY

Now know as *Bromelia antiacantha*, this plant was named *B. fastuosa* by John Lindley. The hand-coloured engraving after a drawing by Lindley is from his *Collectanea botanica* (1821).

20 MONDAY

21 TUESDAY

22 WEDNESDAY   *Full Moon*   *Winter Solstice*

23 THURSDAY

24 FRIDAY   *Christmas Eve*
                                                    Holiday, USA (observed)

25 SATURDAY   *Christmas Day*

26 SUNDAY   *Boxing Day (St Stephen's Day)*

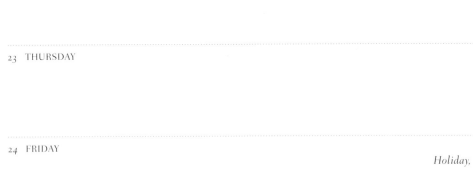

Amaryllis vittata major, now classified as a form of *Hippeastrum vittatum*, a hand-coloured engraving after a drawing by John Lindley from his *Collectanea botanica* (1821)

27   MONDAY   *Holiday, UK, Republic of Ireland, Canada,*
Australia and New Zealand

28   TUESDAY   *Holiday, UK, Republic of Ireland, Canada,*
Australia and New Zealand

29   WEDNESDAY   *Last Quarter*

30   THURSDAY

31   FRIDAY   *Millennium Holiday, UK (to be confirmed)*

1   SATURDAY   *New Year's Day*

2   SUNDAY

Cattleya labiata, a hand-coloured engraving after a drawing by John Lindley from his *Collectanea botanica* (1821). Lindley named the genus, of which this is the type specimen, in honour of his patron William Cattley.

Year Planner
1999

JANUARY
M	T	W	T	F	S	S
				1	2	3
4	5	6	7	8	9	10
11	12	13	14	15	16	17
18	19	20	21	22	23	24
25	26	27	28	29	30	31

FEBRUARY
M	T	W	T	F	S	S
1	2	3	4	5	6	7
8	9	10	11	12	13	14
15	16	17	18	19	20	21
22	23	24	25	26	27	28

MARCH
M	T	W	T	F	S	S
1	2	3	4	5	6	7
8	9	10	11	12	13	14
15	16	17	18	19	20	21
22	23	24	25	26	27	28
29	30	31				

APRIL
M	T	W	T	F	S	S
			1	2	3	
5	6	7	8	9	10	1
12	13	14	15	16	17	1
19	20	21	22	23	24	2
26	27	28	29	30		

MAY
M	T	W	T	F	S	S
					1	2
3	4	5	6	7	8	9
10	11	12	13	14	15	16
17	18	19	20	21	22	23
24	25	26	27	28	29	30
31						

JUNE
M	T	W	T	F	S	S
	1	2	3	4	5	6
7	8	9	10	11	12	13
14	15	16	17	18	19	20
21	22	23	24	25	26	27
28	29	30				

JULY
M	T	W	T	F	S	S
			1	2	3	4
5	6	7	8	9	10	11
12	13	14	15	16	17	18
19	20	21	22	23	24	25
26	27	28	29	30	31	

AUGUST
M	T	W	T	F	S	S
						1
2	3	4	5	6	7	8
9	10	11	12	13	14	1
16	17	18	19	20	21	2
23	24	25	26	27	28	2
30	31					

SEPTEMBER
M	T	W	T	F	S	S
	1	2	3	4	5	
6	7	8	9	10	11	12
13	14	15	16	17	18	19
20	21	22	23	24	25	26
27	28	29	30			

OCTOBER
M	T	W	T	F	S	S
				1	2	3
4	5	6	7	8	9	10
11	12	13	14	15	16	17
18	19	20	21	22	23	24
25	26	27	28	29	30	31

NOVEMBER
M	T	W	T	F	S	S
1	2	3	4	5	6	7
8	9	10	11	12	13	14
15	16	17	18	19	20	21
22	23	24	25	26	27	28
29	30					

DECEMBER
M	T	W	T	F	S	S
		1	2	3	4	
6	7	8	9	10	11	1
13	14	15	16	17	18	1
20	21	22	23	24	25	2
27	28	29	30	31		

2000

JANUARY
M	T	W	T	F	S	S
					1	2
3	4	5	6	7	8	9
10	11	12	13	14	15	16
17	18	19	20	21	22	23
24	25	26	27	28	29	30
31						

FEBRUARY
M	T	W	T	F	S	S
	1	2	3	4	5	6
7	8	9	10	11	12	13
14	15	16	17	18	19	20
21	22	23	24	25	26	27
28	29					

MARCH
M	T	W	T	F	S	S
		1	2	3	4	5
6	7	8	9	10	11	12
13	14	15	16	17	18	19
20	21	22	23	24	25	26
27	28	29	30	31		

APRIL
M	T	W	T	F	S	S
					1	
3	4	5	6	7	8	9
10	11	12	13	14	15	1
17	18	19	20	21	22	2
24	25	26	27	28	29	3

MAY
M	T	W	T	F	S	S
1	2	3	4	5	6	7
8	9	10	11	12	13	14
15	16	17	18	19	20	21
22	23	24	25	26	27	28
29	30	31				

JUNE
M	T	W	T	F	S	S
			1	2	3	4
5	6	7	8	9	10	11
12	13	14	15	16	17	18
19	20	21	22	23	24	25
26	27	28	29	30		

JULY
M	T	W	T	F	S	S
					1	2
3	4	5	6	7	8	9
10	11	12	13	14	15	16
17	18	19	20	21	22	23
24	25	26	27	28	29	30
31						

AUGUST
M	T	W	T	F	S	S
	1	2	3	4	5	
7	8	9	10	11	12	1
14	15	16	17	18	19	2
21	22	23	24	25	26	2
28	29	30	31			

SEPTEMBER
M	T	W	T	F	S	S
				1	2	3
4	5	6	7	8	9	10
11	12	13	14	15	16	17
18	19	20	21	22	23	24
25	26	27	28	29	30	

OCTOBER
M	T	W	T	F	S	S
						1
2	3	4	5	6	7	8
9	10	11	12	13	14	15
16	17	18	19	20	21	22
23	24	25	26	27	28	29
30	31					

NOVEMBER
M	T	W	T	F	S	S
		1	2	3	4	5
6	7	8	9	10	11	12
13	14	15	16	17	18	19
20	21	22	23	24	25	26
27	28	29	30			

DECEMBER
M	T	W	T	F	S	S
				1	2	
4	5	6	7	8	9	1
11	12	13	14	15	16	1
18	19	20	21	22	23	2
25	26	27	28	29	30	3